Lots of Nuts

Written by Gill Munton

Illustrated by Emma Dodson

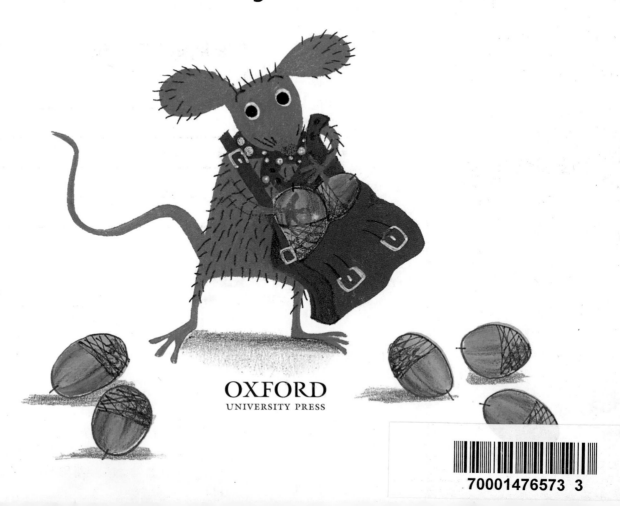

OXFORD

UNIVERSITY PRESS

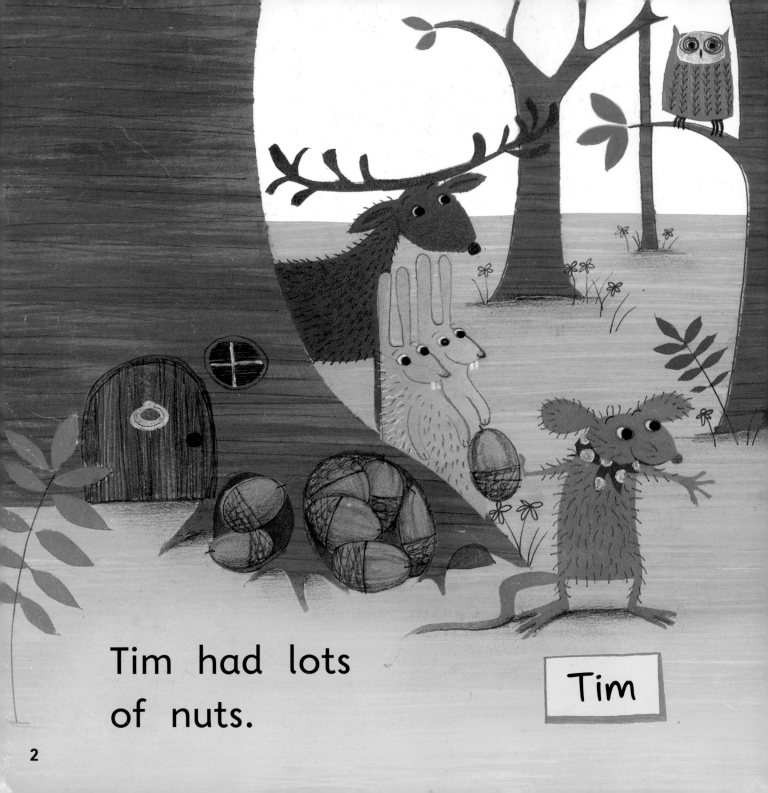

Tim had lots
of nuts.

Tim

2

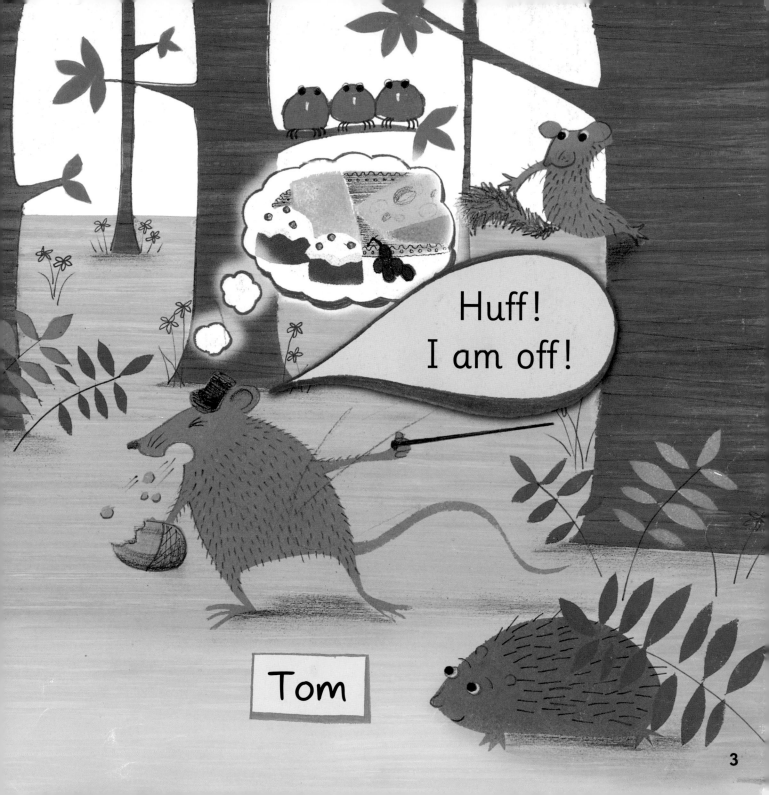

Huff!
I am off!

Tom

3

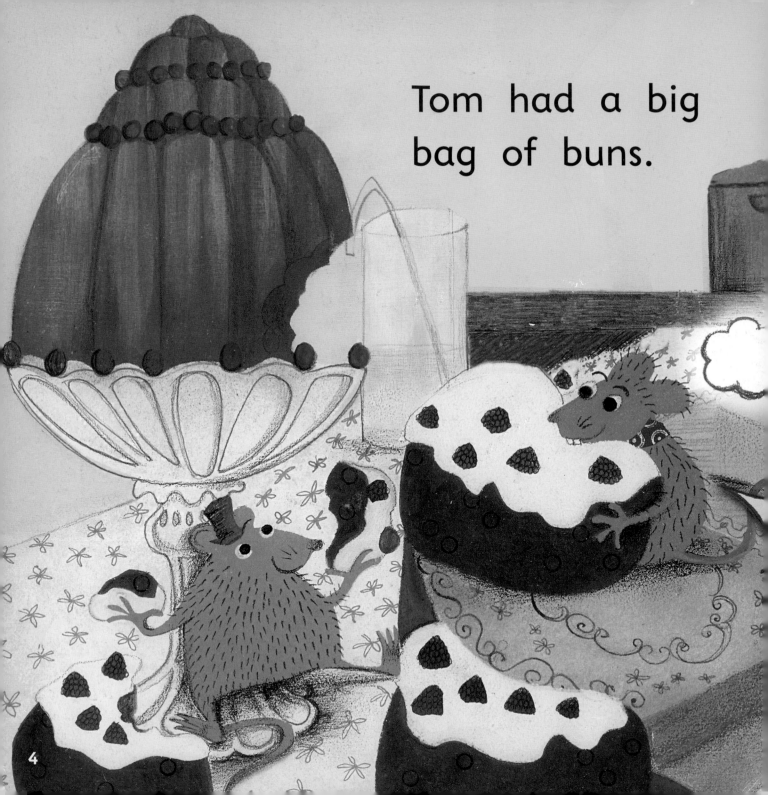

Tom had a big bag of buns.

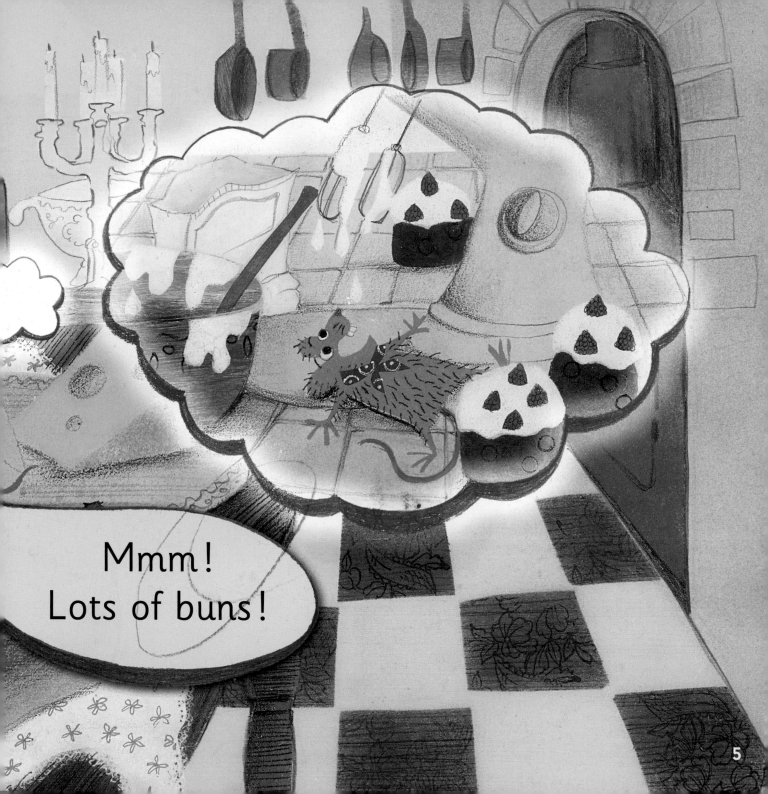

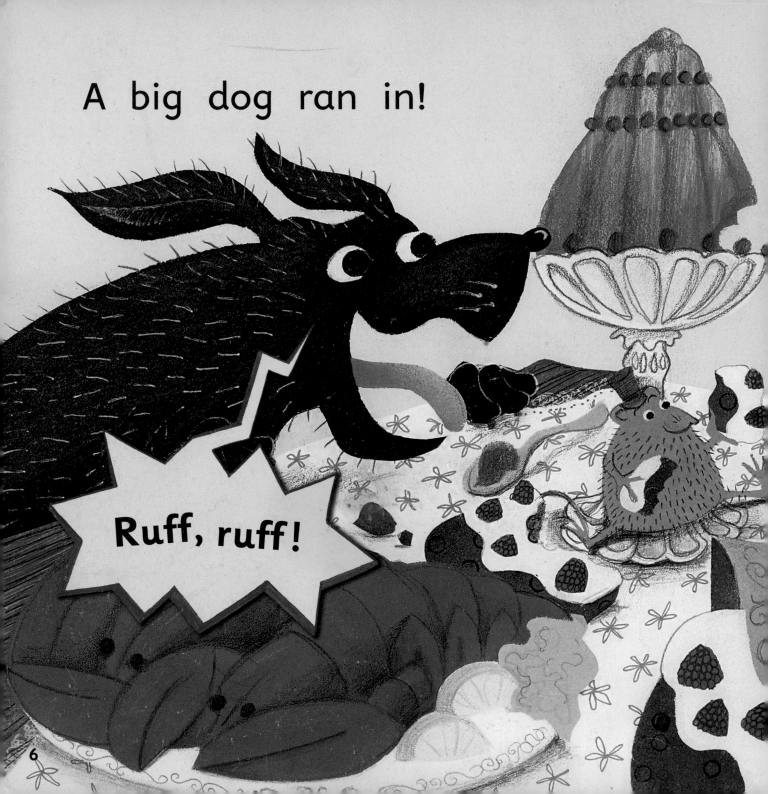

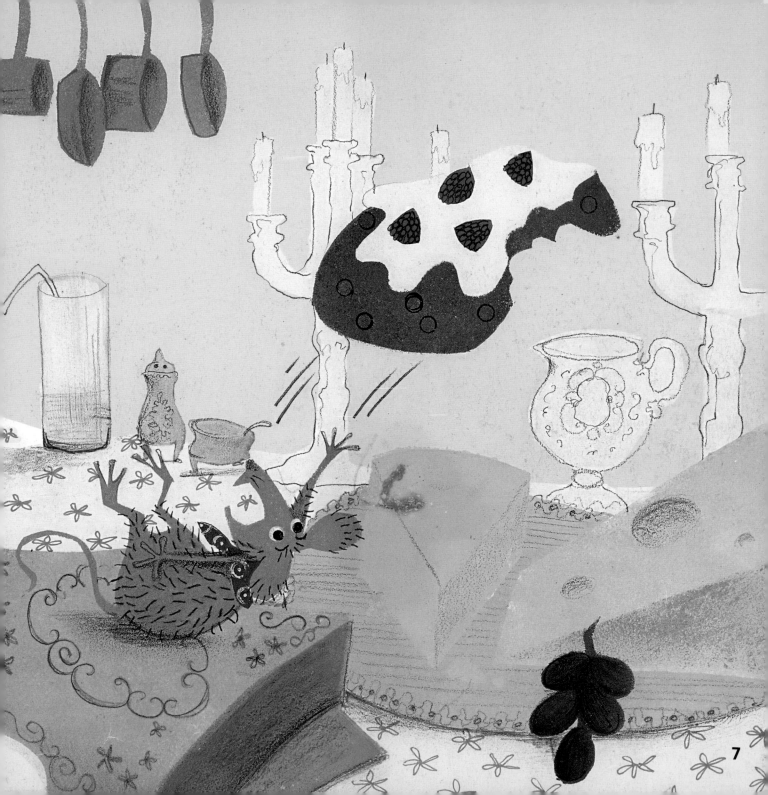

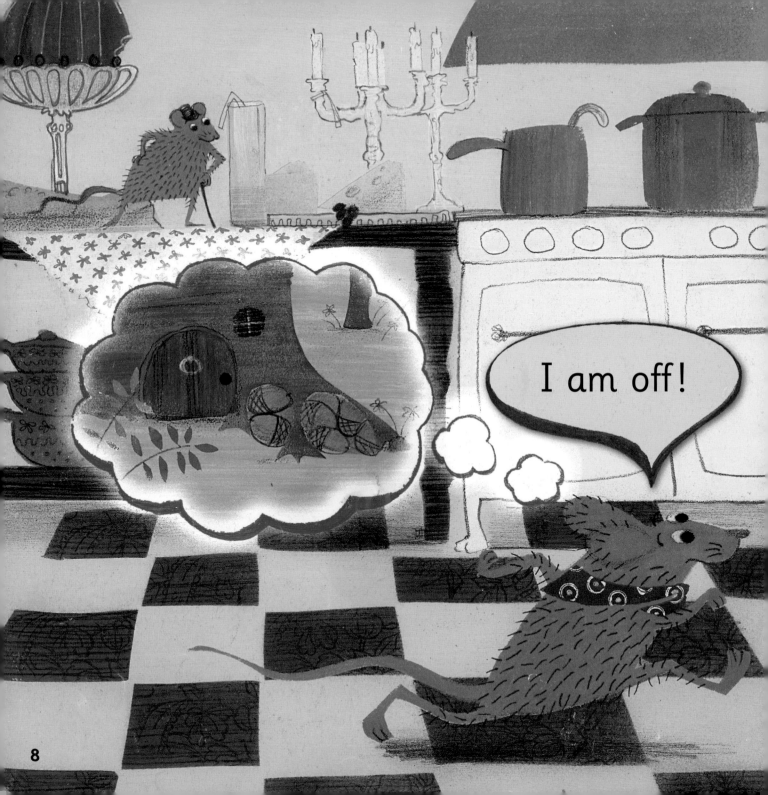

8

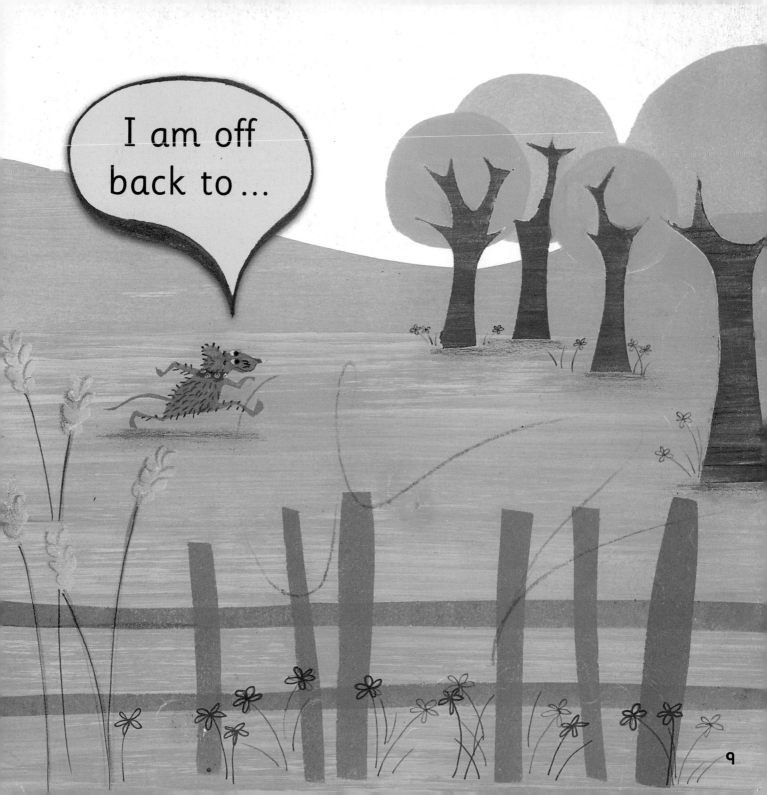

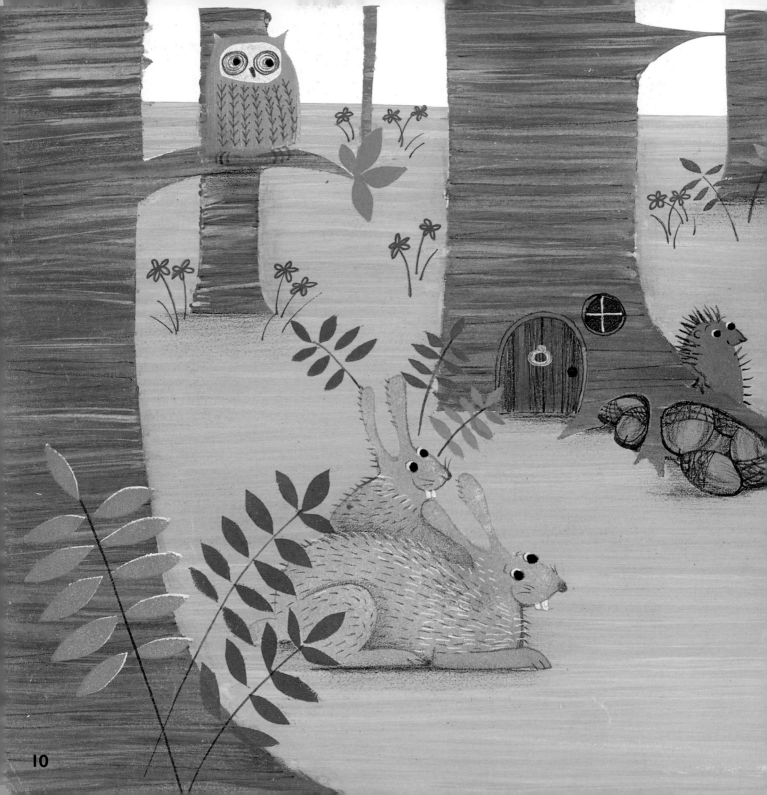

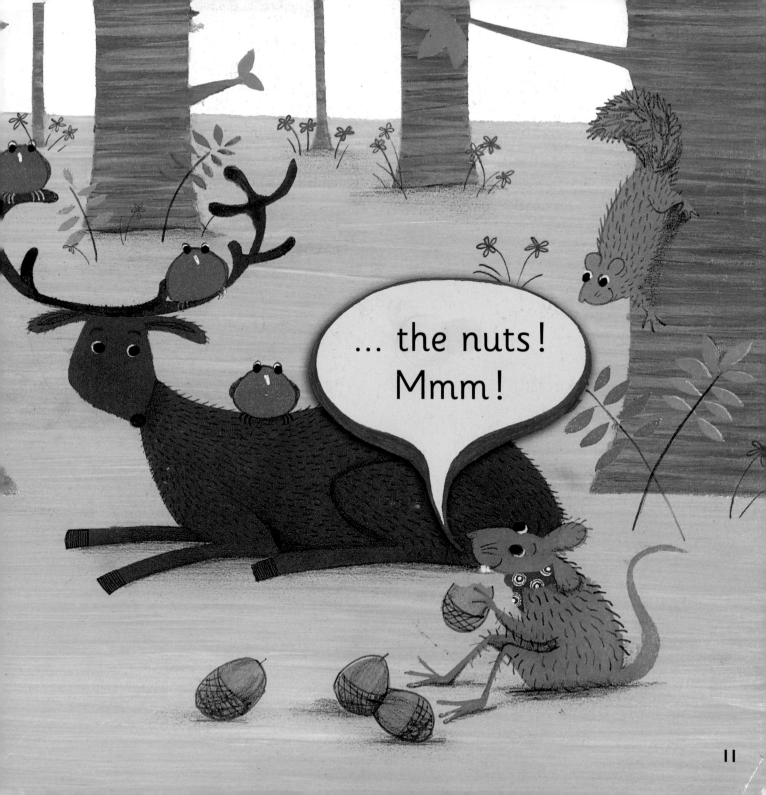

Retell the story

Once upon a time...

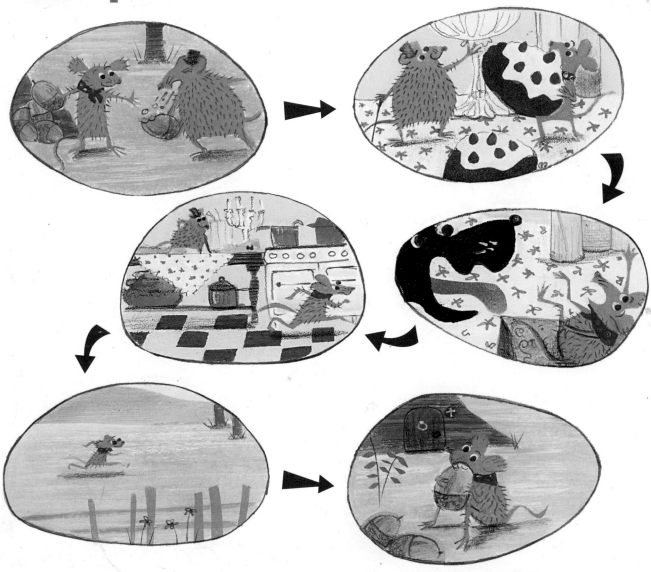

The end.